This book belongs to

....

Quarto is the authority on a wide range of topics.

Quarto educates, entertains and enriches the lives of our readers—enthusiasts and lovers of hands-on living.

www.quartoknows.com

© 2018 Quarto Publishing plc

First published in 2018 by QED Publishing, an imprint of The Quarto Group. The Old Brewery, 6 Blundell Street, London N7 9BH, United Kingdom. T (0)20 7700 6700 F (0)20 7700 8066 www.QuartoKnows.com

A catalogue record for this book is available from the British Library.

ISBN 978-1-91241-385-0

Based on the original story by Steve Smallman

Author of adapted text: Katie Woolley
Series Editor: Joyce Bentley
Series Designer: Sarah Peden

Manufactured in Dongguan, China TL042018

9 8 7 6 5 4 3 2 1

MIX
Paper from responsible sources
FSC® C104723
FSC
www.fsc.org

Reading
Gems

Percy
Penguin

All the penguins were perfect.

But Percy Penguin was not perfect.

Percy did not eat fish nicely.

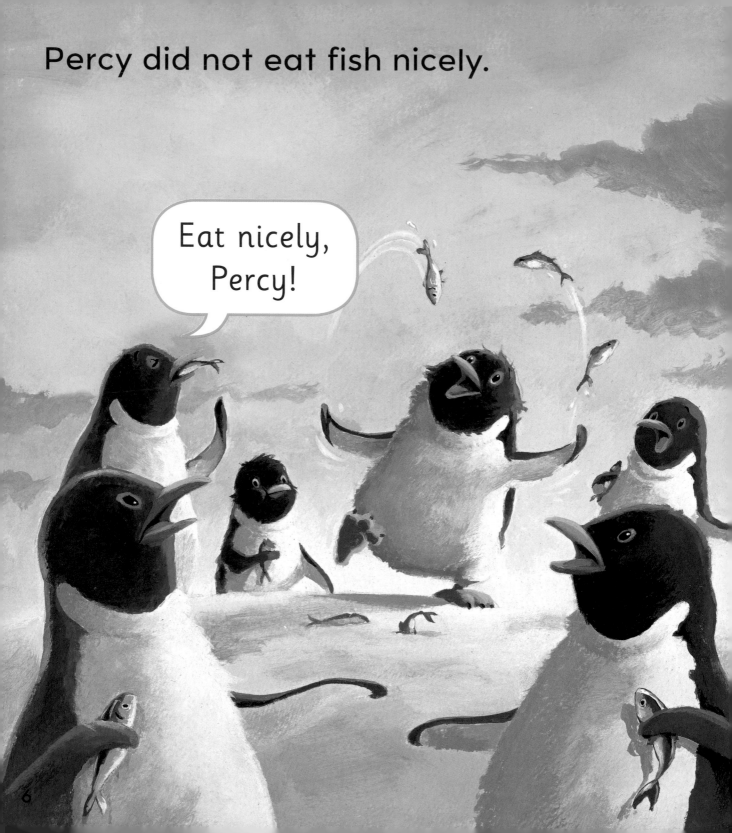

He did not waddle slowly.

Waddle slowly, Percy!

Percy did not swim nicely.

You are a silly penguin.

The penguins all cuddled up.

But Percy made a big smell.

Percy, you smell!

Percy was sad. He waddled off
in the snow.

He made a snow penguin
to cuddle.

All the penguins were sad.

They waddled off to find him.

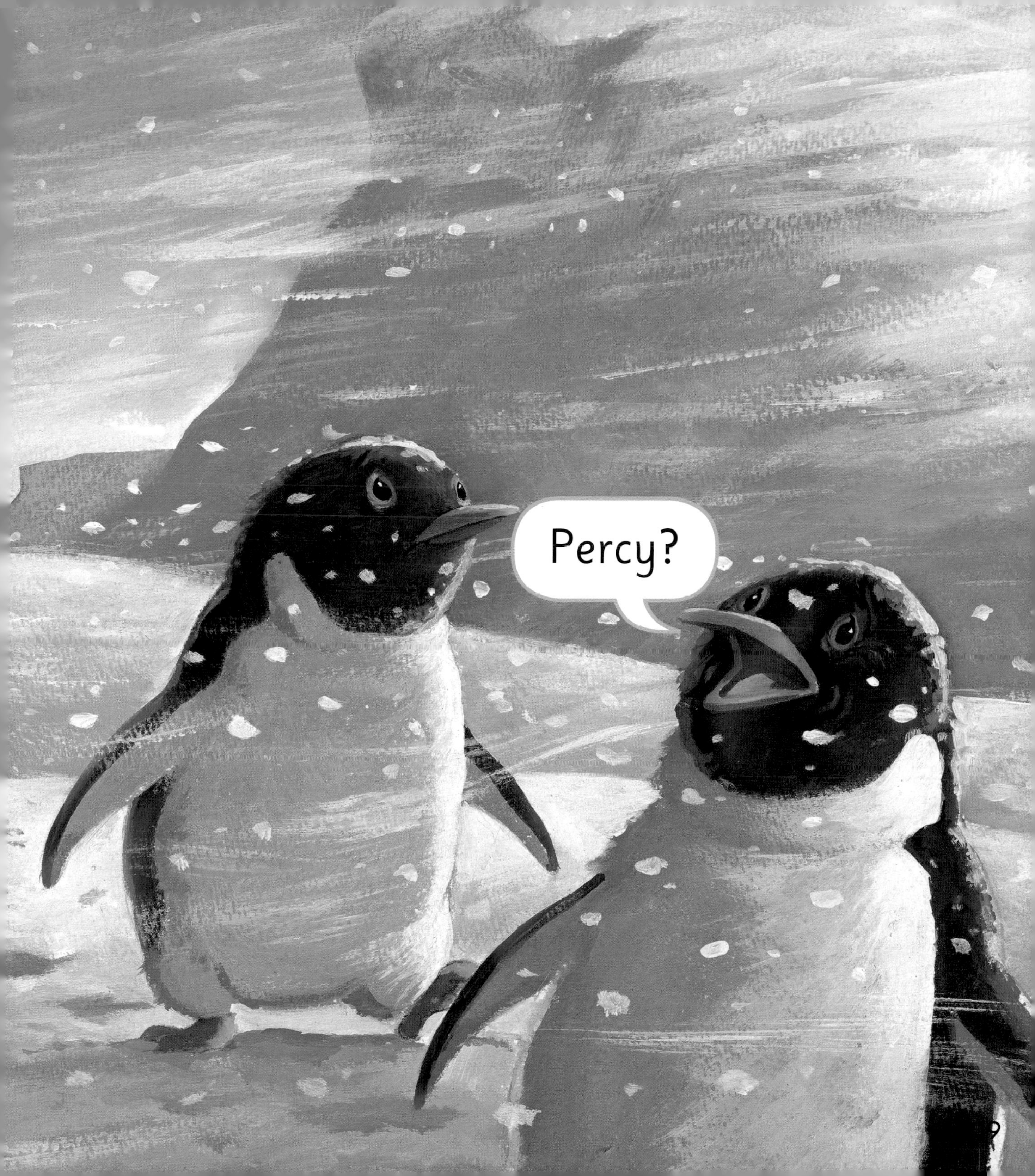
Percy?

The penguins did find Percy.

They all cuddled up to him.

We missed you, Percy!

Story Words

cuddle

eat

fish

penguin

Percy

smell

snow penguin

swim

waddle

Let's Talk About Percy Penguin

Look carefully at the book cover.

Talk about the habitat the penguins live in.

Is it hot or cold?

Do you think penguins feel the cold?

What makes Percy different in this story?

Is it good to be different?

What qualities does Percy have that the other penguins don't?

The story is all about accepting differences.

The penguins realise it's good to be different. They miss Percy's fun-loving nature. Think about your friends. What differences do you have?

How do you think Percy feels when the other penguins don't want him?

Have you ever felt left out?

How did it make you feel?

Did you like the story?

What was your favourite part?

Fun and Games

Look at the pictures. What are they?
What letter sound does each word begin with?
Follow the trails to see if you are right!

cuddle   happy   smell   sad

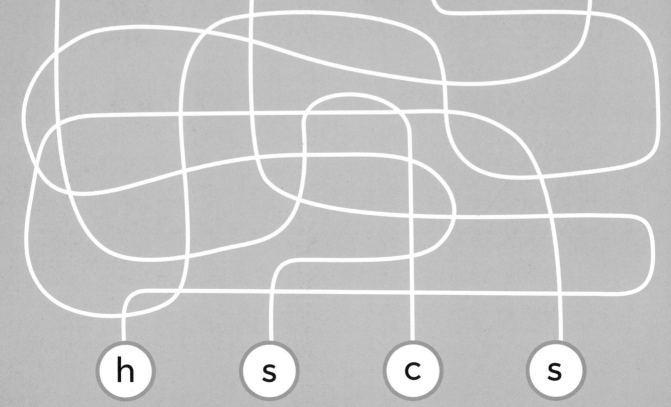

h   s   c   s

Penguins live in a cold place. Look at the pictures and read the words. Which word does not match its picture?

warm

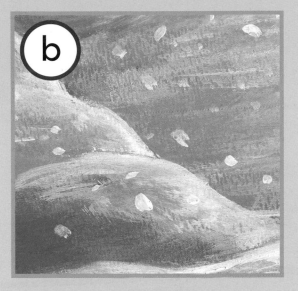

snow

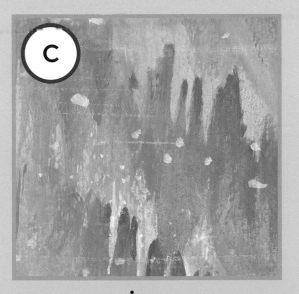

ice

snow penguin

Your Turn

Now that you have read the story,
have a go at telling it in your own words.
Use the pictures below to help you.

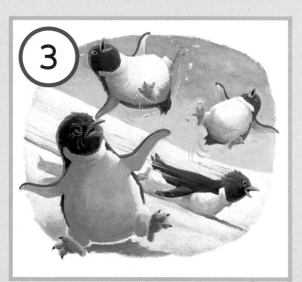

GET TO KNOW READING GEMS

Reading Gems is a series of books that has been written for children who are learning to read. The books have been created in consultation with a literacy specialist.

The books fit into four levels, with each level getting more challenging as a child's confidence and reading ability grows. The simple text and fun illustrations provide gradual, structured practice of reading. Most importantly, these books are good stories that are fun to read!

Level 1 is for children who are taking their first steps into reading. Story themes and subjects are familiar to young children, and there is lots of repetition to build reading confidence.

Level 2 is for children who have taken their first reading steps and are becoming readers. Story themes are still familiar but sentences are a bit longer, as children begin to tackle more challenging vocabulary.

Level 3 is for children who are developing as readers. Stories and subjects are varied, and more descriptive words are introduced.

Level 4 is for readers who are rapidly growing in reading confidence and independence. There is less repetition on the page, broader themes are explored and plot lines straddle multiple pages.

Percy Penguin is all about a group of penguins who think Percy is a nuisance. It explores themes of friendship and accepting each other's differences.

Level 1

All the penguins were perfect.
But Percy Penguin was not perfect.

Short sentences ✓

Simple vocabulary ✓

Lots of repetition ✓

Pictures and words support one another ✓